TOM GATES

BIG BOOK OF FUN STUFF

YES!

BIG WOOF!

By LIZ PICHON

MINE!

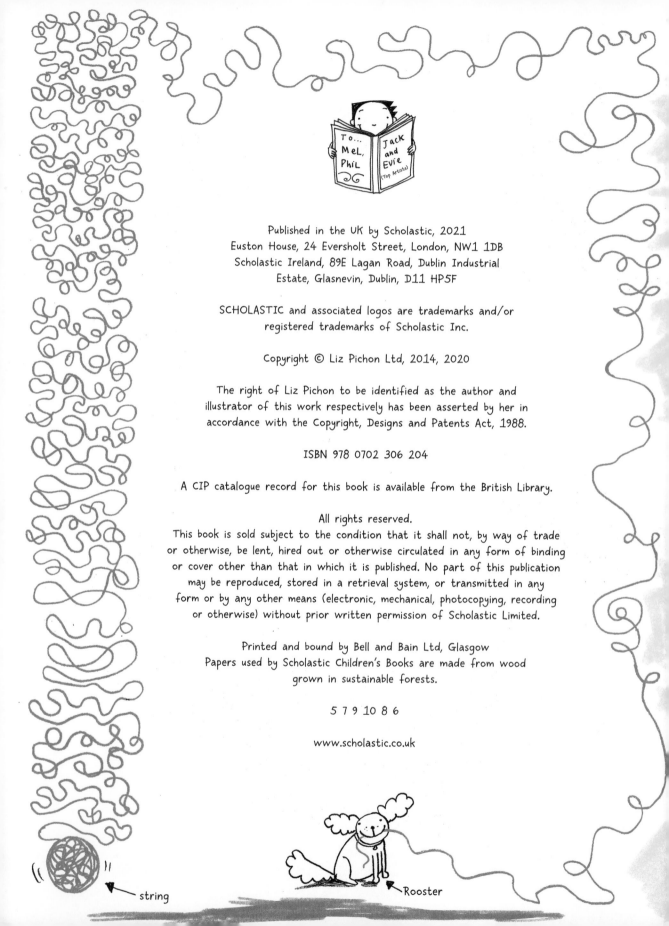

To... Mel, Phil

Jack and Evie (Top Artists)

Published in the UK by Scholastic, 2021
Euston House, 24 Eversholt Street, London, NW1 1DB
Scholastic Ireland, 89E Lagan Road, Dublin Industrial
Estate, Glasnevin, Dublin, D11 HP5F

SCHOLASTIC and associated logos are trademarks and/or
registered trademarks of Scholastic Inc.

ISBN 978 0702 306 204

A CIP catalogue record for this book is available from the British Library.

Printed and bound by Bell and Bain Ltd, Glasgow
Papers used by Scholastic Children's Books are made from wood
grown in sustainable forests.

5 7 9 10 8 6

www.scholastic.co.uk

string

Rooster

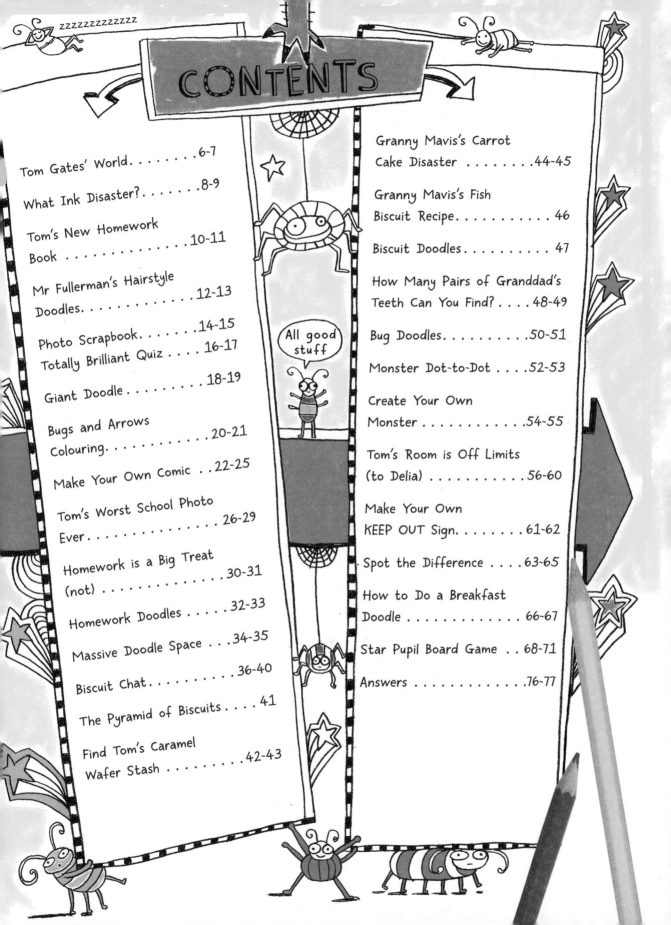

CONTENTS

All good stuff

WHAT INK DISASTER?

(This one --------------->)

Turning my accidental INK SPLODGE
into finger prints, bugs and A GIANT BIRD
was inspired (I think).

What can YOU make the other finger prints into?
Have a go, it's all dry now.

What GIANT bird?

Mr Fullerman has given [me] ☺ THIS book →

which is

HUGE

The whole class have got one each. We have to fill them up
with all kinds of things we can't fit in our normal-size
books. Which is EXCELLENT news, and means I can create
doodles, puzzles, stories and more doodles in it.

STARTING with decorating the FRONT COVER!

Mr Fullerman reminds us,

 "There'll be some HOMEWORK to do too."

(Great!)   But for NOW I'll
get doodling...

Get
doodling

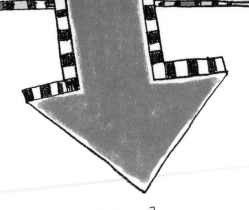

Mr Fullerman has given us this reminder about the school photograph tomorrow. While he's handing the rest out, and telling us to wear a proper uniform (that kind of thing), I get to doodle on my rubber.

Ha! Ha!

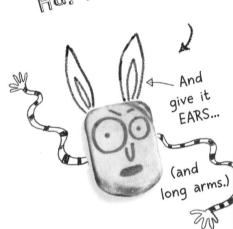

And give it EARS...

(and long arms.)

Oakwood School
REMINDER

The school photographer will be coming to take lovely, cheery photographs of all the pupils.

If your child has brothers or sisters in the school and you'd like a group photo, fill in the form below.

Name.................... Class.............

Brother/sister...............................

LUCKILY for ME I avoided having a photo with Delia.

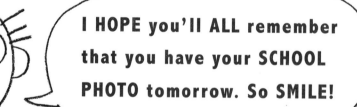

I HOPE you'll ALL remember that you have your SCHOOL PHOTO tomorrow. So SMILE!

As he's talking, I can see some SUNLIGHT bouncing off the top of his head. It's like a little STAR twinkling, making it look like he's got SHINY, happy hair. Which makes me WONDER what he'd look like ...

12

(Go on ... have a go!)

Wobble
hair
HA, HA!

HERE ARE SOME MORE PHOTOS
(to laugh at ... HA! HA! HA!)

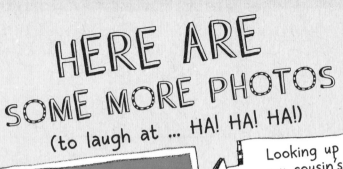

No way!

(BISCUIT TREATS to keep me going)

Looking up my cousin's nose... NICE!

A RARE picture of DELIA hugging me. See how nervous I look...

(For good reason)

Took me ages to get Delia to stand in the right spot.

Sharing a photo booth with Delia was NEVER easy.

WHO'S THAT with dodgy hair?

Mum and Dad kissing... I can't LOOK... (YUCK!)

Here's a photo of Dad with HAIR!

I loved this bunny wearing Delia's sunglasses.

Ha!

14

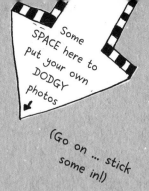

Some SPACE here to put your own DODGY photos ↓

(Go on ... stick some in!)

Sorry to BUTT in here, but I thought I'd share this school photo of ME looking GRUMPIER than DELIA. I'd been told off for being "SILLY", so I SULKED instead. And here's the result. (SHAME!)

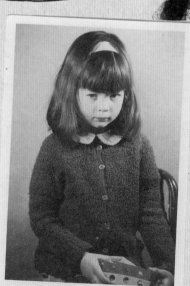

I did learn how to smile a bit in pictures. See!

IT'S HERE!

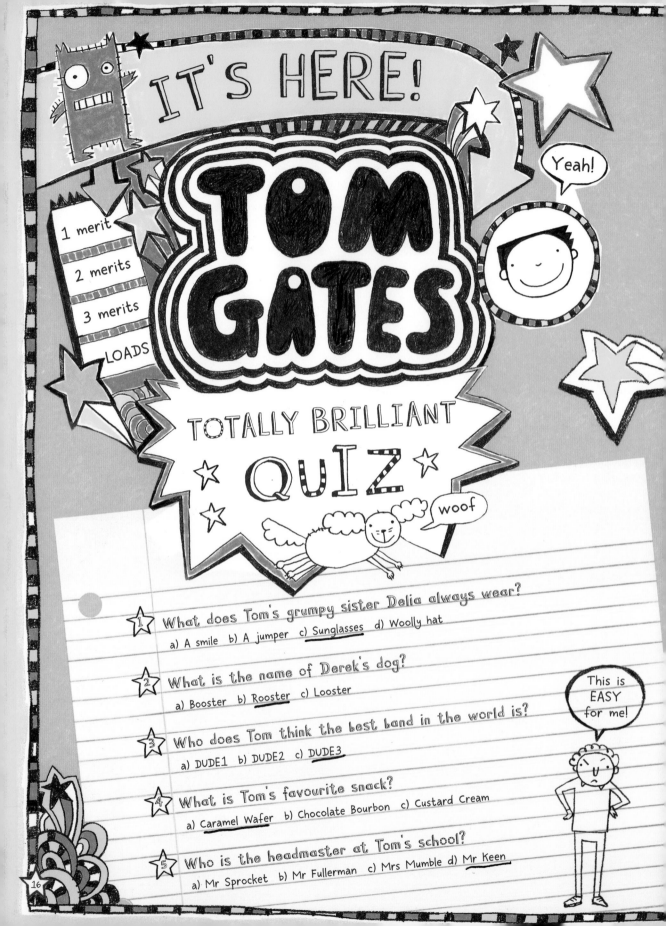

Yeah!

TOM GATES

1 merit
2 merits
3 merits
LOADS

TOTALLY BRILLIANT ☆ QUIZ ☆

woof

This is EASY for me!

⭐ 1 **What does Tom's grumpy sister Delia always wear?**
   a) A smile   b) A jumper   c) Sunglasses   d) Woolly hat

⭐ 2 **What is the name of Derek's dog?**
   a) Booster   b) Rooster   c) Looster

⭐ 3 **Who does Tom think the best band in the world is?**
   a) DUDE1   b) DUDE2   c) DUDE3

⭐ 4 **What is Tom's favourite snack?**
   a) Caramel Wafer   b) Chocolate Bourbon   c) Custard Cream

⭐ 5 **Who is the headmaster at Tom's school?**
   a) Mr Sprocket   b) Mr Fullerman   c) Mrs Mumble   d) Mr Keen

Top Score! → 😊   Rubbish score 😞

Whatever...

⭐ 6 **What does Tom call his grandparents?**
a) The Aliens   b) The Wrinklies   c) The Fossils

⭐ 7 **What does Mr Fullerman catch Tom doing in class?**
a) Doodling   b) Singing   c) Whistling

⭐ 8 **What did Granny Mavis once put on a pizza for Tom?**
a) A pineapple   b) A banana   c) A mango   d) A coconut

⭐ 9 **Who is Tom's best friend?**
a) Amy   b) Marcus   c) Derek

⭐ 10 **What song does Tom write about Delia?**
a) Delia's a weirdo   b) Delia's a biscuit thief   c) Delia's the best sister ever

⭐ 11 **How much does Tom like camping?**
a) A lot   b) It's the best holiday ever   c) Not very much

⭐ 12 **Who sits next to Tom in class?**
a) Derek and Rooster   b) Brad and Mark   c) Marcus and Amy   d) Marcus and Florence

⭐ 13 **What is Mrs Worthington's nickname?**
a) Mrs Worthy   b) Mrs Worthingtoenail   c) Mrs Worthingtash

TOP SCORE YEAH!

Beady eyes →

One of the FUN things I like to do is HIDE Delia's sunglasses. See if you can find them and colour in the doodle if you have the time (it's BIG!).

COLOUR
IN THE
BUGS AND
ARROWS

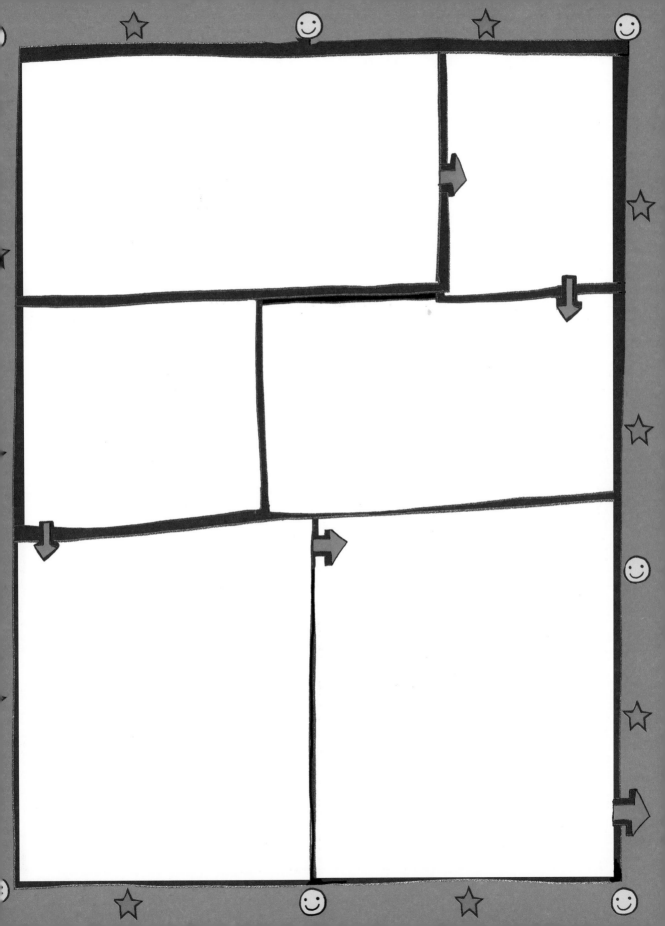

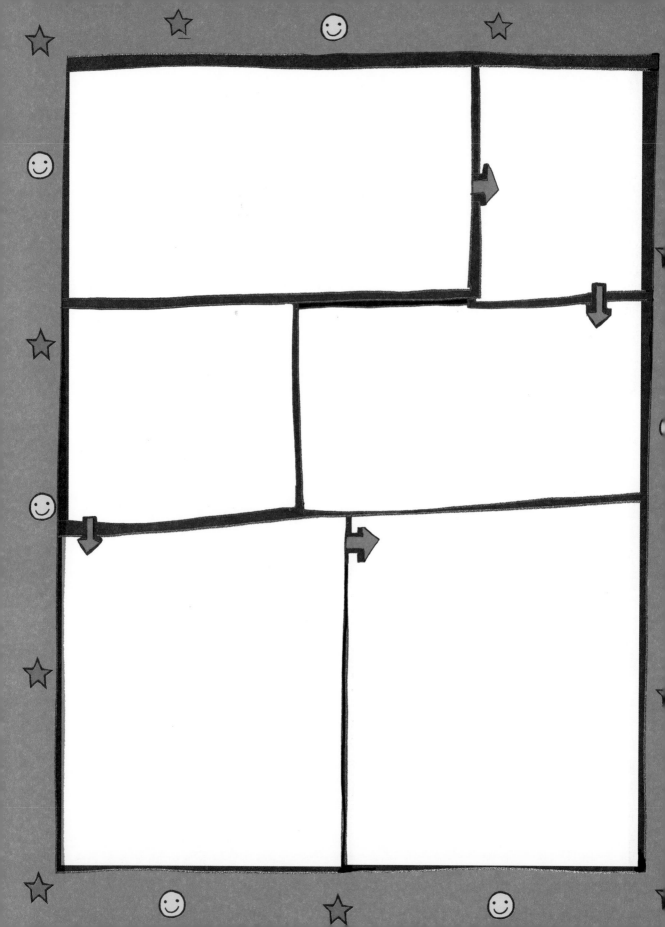

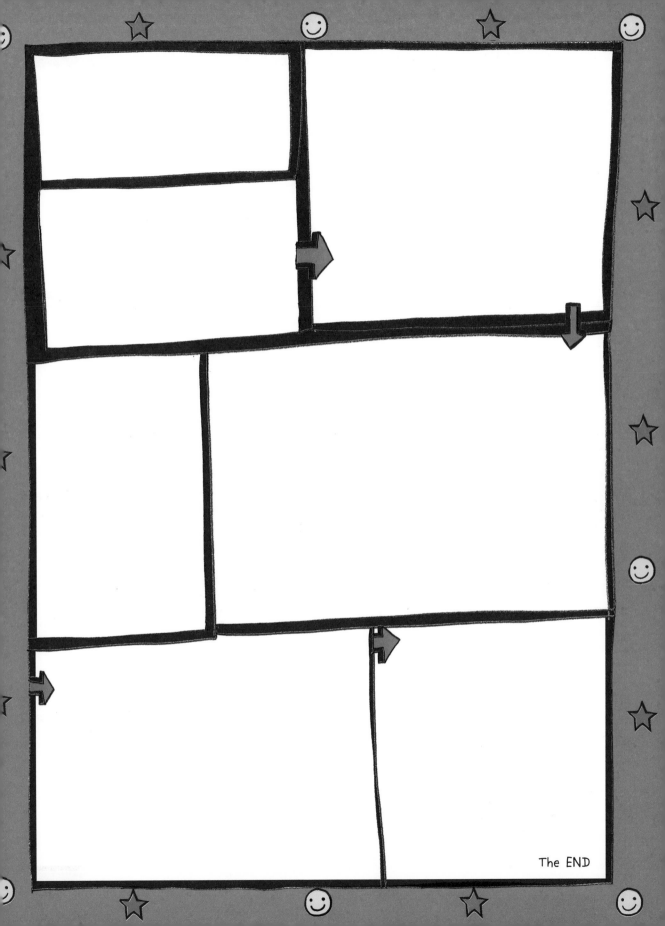

The END

Every year we have a school PHOTO taken, which SOMEHOW always manages to be a **DISASTER** ⇨ for me (see THE BRILLIANT WORLD OF TOM GATES, p75).

Thanks to Mum putting my dodgy pictures in PHOTO FRAMES, hanging them on walls, → or arranging them into little collections, even if I wanted to forget about them ... I CAN'T.

↖ Baby picture with drool

They're ALL OVER the **PLACE!**

It's not like I don't try to SMILE or do as the photographer asks me to. It just never seems to work out.

SEE EVIDENCE ⇨

Delia

This is what happened when I was waiting in line to have my FIRST EVER school photo taken. I watched the photographer use a funny **RABBIT** puppet to make the children LAUGH. He pretended the rabbit was saying SILLY things in a SQUEAKY voice. Which seemed to work and got the kids to smile for their photos. When it was MY turn, I sat down and got ready to be ENTERTAINED by the Squeaky Rabbit.

(top button done up) →

But for SOME reason the photographer decided to SWAP props and use an old-fashioned bike horn instead.

HONK

HUH?

I was too startled to smile.
(The noise made me jump out of the chair.)

Then he did it AGAIN. And I said AGH!

which made the photographer REALIZE it wasn't making me laugh.
So he got the rabbit back out to SQUEAK a joke at me instead.

He said (or the RABBIT said),

Hello Tom, why did the chicken cross the  PLAYGROUND?

(I shook my head because I didn't know.)

To get to the OTHER ... SLIDE Ha! Ha! Ha!

It was quite funny and made me smile. I'd almost forgotten
about having my photo taken – RIGHT up until the FLASH went off
and the rabbit said I could go back to class.

BYE TOM! Then a couple of weeks later, Marcus Meldrew
volunteered to hand out the ENVELOPES which had our photos
in them to everyone in the class. When it came to ME, he LOOKED at my
photo and told me what he thought. (Like I wanted to know.)

"You look WEIRD," he said.

"Really Marcus – who asked YOU?" I said, just wanting
to see my photo for MYSELF.

(Turns out I did look a bit ... SURPRISED!)

I decided NOT to show Mum my school
photo and keep it in my bag (for ever). But she found
it anyway. What's this?   Mum told me I looked REALLY CUTE!

I started to think that maybe it wasn't so bad after all.

But then my grumpy sister Delia leant over Mum's shoulder – LAUGHED – HA! HA! and told me I had (FROG EYES) in the photo. (Which I thought was RICH coming from her, as Delia's school photos weren't EXACTLY cheery.)

"At least you can see my eyes and MUM thinks I look CUTE," I told her.

(...for a frog) she added before Mum said, "That's enough both of you."

But however SHOCKED I looked in [THAT] school photo, it wasn't the WORST one I've had done. My YEAR TWO picture was even worse. I remember the day I had it taken – it started off OK.

Mr Fullerman reminded our class that AFTER breaktime we'd all be going to the hall for the school photo. **Don't forget!** he added.

But I got involved in a REALLY **EPIC** game of CHAMP

(see how to play CHAMP in EVERYTHING'S AMAZING (SORT OF) on page 31).

And all that running around and hitting the ball back and forth meant I'd got a bit PUFFED out and sweaty.

So before my photo was taken, I took off my sweatshirt, which helped me to cool down a bit, and I even remembered to pat down my hair. EVERYTHING seemed to go smoothly and the photographer was happy enough. (Very good!)

I didn't realize EXACTLY HOW HOT and sweaty that game of CHAMP had made me until the photo arrived. My FACE looked like a BIG RED TOMATO.

"Didn't the photographer say anything to you?" Mum asked me when she saw it.

"What, like – your face looks like a RED tomato? No, she didn't." It still didn't stop Mum from ordering LOADS of copies though. Some of them were in BLACK AND WHITE (which I thought made my face look even WORSE).

Mum's put THAT particular PHOTO on the STAIRCASE wall. Whenever Delia walks past it, she likes to mutter things like "TRAGIC" or "BEETROOT" under her breath. Especially if I'm around. (Which is annoying.) SO...

HERE are my **TOP TIPS** up with RUBBISH on HOW NOT to end school photos:

1 Try to remember WHAT DAY the school photo is being taken. (It helps...)

WHAT photo?

2 Scoffing MESSY food beforehand is NOT a good idea.

YUM — crumbs, ketchup

3 Don't SMILE SO much that your eyes disappear.

cheese

4 And don't try and be "COOL", you'll end up looking like you have a toothache, or miserable.

SO to PROVE that I'm not the ONLY person in my family that's had a few (OK ... a lot of) dodgy photos, I'm on a MISSION to find some other ones.

 Which involves RUMMAGING around in the photo box.

I'M NOT DISAPPOINTED. There are LOADS.

 Including some of **THE FOSSILS** when Granddad had TEETH (and they were much younger).

AND Delia's SCHOOL PHOTOS.

Ha! Ha! This one is from when Delia cut her OWN hair with PLAY scissors! (It looks like a BIRD'S NEST.)

Here's Mum and Dad – DAD has HAIR! And if I did this in a photo, Mum would be CROSS.

When Mr Fullerman  handed out our ENGLISH worksheets, he told us that if we didn't have time to finish it in class we could **Take it HOME to do.**

Like it was a BIG TREAT or something. (It's not.

I try really hard to get my work done in class, but for some reason it doesn't work out.

(me working)

Some people in my class ALWAYS manage to get all their work done. AND do their homework as well.

Like Amy Porter and Leroy Lewis.

Other kids (like me) aren't quite so good at remembering to bring it in. Mind you, Amber Tutley Green had a brilliant excuse the other day. She said her dad washed it in her coat pocket. I made a NOTE of that one.

Homework EXCUSE

My Dad washed my clothes and my homework was in the pocket. It's RUINED now.

Mark Clump's excuses are always REALLY FUNNY. He told Mr Fullerman,

My pet snake ate my homework, Sir...

Mr Fullerman didn't believe him.

"REALLY, MARK?" he said, until Mark showed him a photo of his snake. Which we all wanted to see. It was very impressive.

I'd forgotten to do my short poem last week and when Mr Fullerman asked me where it was, I only went and BLURTED out...

"My dog chewed it up, Sir!"

Which was a RUBBISH excuse. Mostly because ...

I don't have a dog. (I'd forgotten about THAT!)

Unfortunately for me, Marcus Meldrew hadn't. He put up his hand and said...

 "Mr FULLERMAN - TOM DOESN'T HAVE A DOG!"

(Thanks a LOT Marcus!) So I said, "YES I DO!"

followed by the first thing I could think of that came into my head.

 It's a SAUSAGE! I mean a sausage dog.

Which made EVERYONE laugh. Mr Fullerman wasn't convinced

and suggested I had plenty of time to start a NEW poem.

"RIGHT NOW TOM." I didn't have much choice... sigh.

It wasn't the BEST thing I'd ever written. But it was short (and TRUE!)

My Short Poem - By Tom Gates

I want a dog, I want a dog
I want a dog, And not a frog
The End

From now on I'm going to keep a list of excuses to take a sneaky look at if I get

stuck. Some of them are REAL EXCUSES that have ACTUALLY happened to me

(some are a bit made up).

HA! HA!

HOMEWORK EXCUSES
☆ Aliens took my homework.
☆ I dropped my school bag in a puddle
   and it all got wet.
☆ Marcus Meldrew took my book home
   by accident, so I couldn't do my work.
☆ I LOST it in my messy bedroom.
☆ My cousins hid my book under some cushions.
☆ The wind swept it away.

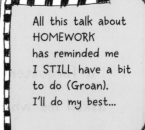 All this talk about HOMEWORK has reminded me I STILL have a bit to do (Groan). I'll do my best...

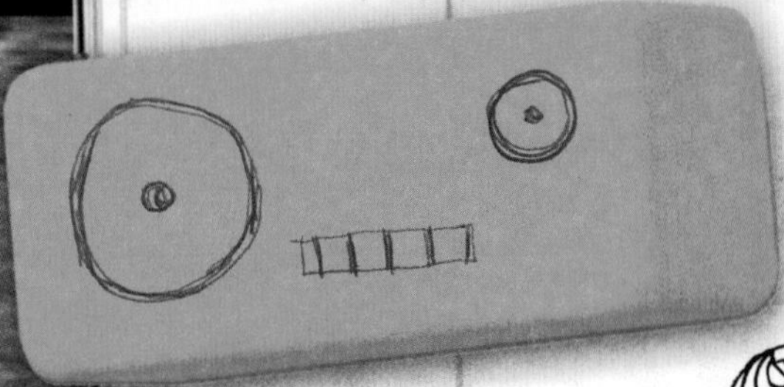

HoMEWORK

I had some homework and I was going to do it,

BUT it's taken me a while just to write the word

HOMEWORK (like you do). THEN, as I was colouring

in the word HOMEWORK, I accidentally started

drawing THIS creature in the middle of my book.

Which was a lot more FUN than doing my homework.

(I hadn't forgotten about it.)

SEE, there's a maths sum ... oh, and a squiggle

that I did while I was thinking about how to do the

maths. Looking at the squiggle, I wondered

WHAT I could turn it into. It was a

CHALLENGE! So I did it

in pencil first. Then I did another.

$$\begin{array}{r} 237 \\ +549 \\ \hline 786 \\ \hline {\scriptstyle 1} \end{array}$$

Hairstyle!

Ha! Ha!

Food

And before I knew it, I'd done ONE MORE!

But because I had to do my homework, I stopped

doing squiggles. (Well... I did this one because it looked

like a monster.)

665
−192
473

I did JUST a few more squiggles FOR LATER.
(Or you could make them into something, if you want?)

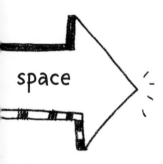

space

I'm at home with Derek  (my BEST mate and next-door neighbour) who's come round to my house so we can do our homework together.

Sigh (We both have to answer questions on the SAME book, so it should be EASY.)

Well, that's the PLAN anyway. But somehow we ALWAYS end up chatting about other really IMPORTANT things like what happened at school yesterday.

I tell Derek, "It was HILARIOUS when Mark Clump dropped his pencil, then climbed under his desk to get it."

"What's funny about that?" Derek asks.

So I stand up and start to ACT OUT the WHOLE story for him.

"Mr Fullerman was taking the register while Mark Clump was looking for his pencil."

(I get on the floor to pretend to be Mark Clump.)

Oh no!

"He found his pencil right next to Solid's legs, which gave him an idea.

"Mark tickled Solid's leg with the pencil then told him he thought something had crawled up it."

Then I demonstrate on Derek by tickling his leg. OI!

36

"Solid thought it was a BUG so huh? he LEAPT

out of his seat and started SHAKING his legs about."
I show Derek what Solid looked like, which Derek thinks is funny.

Derek laughing

me being Solid → I carry on...

"This is the really GOOD bit, Solid actually LOOKED like he was DANCING,
so the whole class starts CLAPPING in TIME when he HOPS.
It was SO funny EVEN Mr Fullerman stopped calling the register and started
laughing ... but not for long."

lap
ap

(I'm still hopping up and down as I tell Derek what happened).

"HEY, I almost forgot," Derek says (in-between laughing),
and TIPS out the entire contents of his bag on to his homework book.
Ha! "I brought these!" he adds.
Ha!
It looks like a half-eaten packet of **CUSTARD CREAMS**.
(Not my favourite biscuits, but I'd eat them anyway.)
Seeing the biscuits I remember I have a WHOLE pound coin that Granny Mavis
gave me for helping to carry her bags the other day (helpful grandson).
"Let's eat these then go to the shop and
spend the pound on something else," I suggest to Derek.
"Ok, let's," he agrees.
(Homework can wait a bit longer. We're on a MISSION to get more
biscuits with my POUND. Or more if I can find any SPARE change.)

£1

CUST
CREAM

When Derek 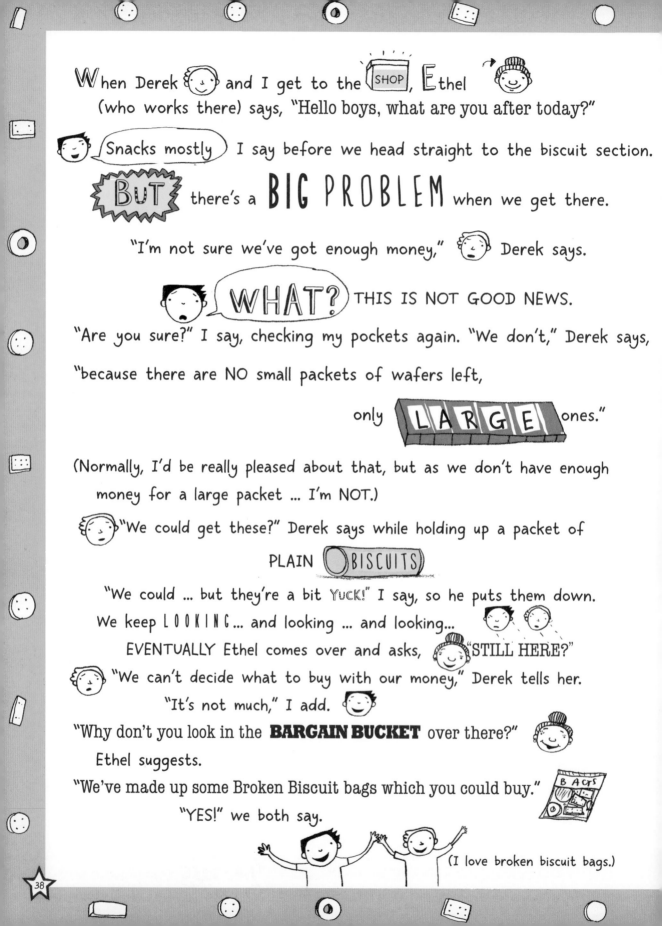 and I get to the SHOP, Ethel (who works there) says, "Hello boys, what are you after today?"

Snacks mostly I say before we head straight to the biscuit section.

BUT there's a BIG PROBLEM when we get there.

"I'm not sure we've got enough money," Derek says.

WHAT? THIS IS NOT GOOD NEWS.

"Are you sure?" I say, checking my pockets again. "We don't," Derek says,

"because there are NO small packets of wafers left,

only LARGE ones."

(Normally, I'd be really pleased about that, but as we don't have enough money for a large packet ... I'm NOT.)

"We could get these?" Derek says while holding up a packet of

PLAIN BISCUITS

"We could ... but they're a bit YUCK!" I say, so he puts them down.
We keep LOOKING... and looking ... and looking...
EVENTUALLY Ethel comes over and asks, "STILL HERE?"

"We can't decide what to buy with our money," Derek tells her.
"It's not much," I add.

"Why don't you look in the **BARGAIN BUCKET** over there?"
Ethel suggests.

"We've made up some Broken Biscuit bags which you could buy."
"YES!" we both say.

(I love broken biscuit bags.)

Because even though BR⊙KEN biscuits might look a bit ... well, broken, they all taste the same. AND you get loads in a bag too.

(It's a RESULT!)

Back at home, Derek and I empty ALL the biscuits on to my table and divide them equally between us. There's an EXCELLENT selection. "This was SUCH a good idea!" Derek says

(I AGREE).

"Speaking of good ideas," I say to Derek in-between mouthfuls. Then I show him how to do a biscuit doodle. These work particularly well with the round biscuits with a hole in them. Ha! Ha!

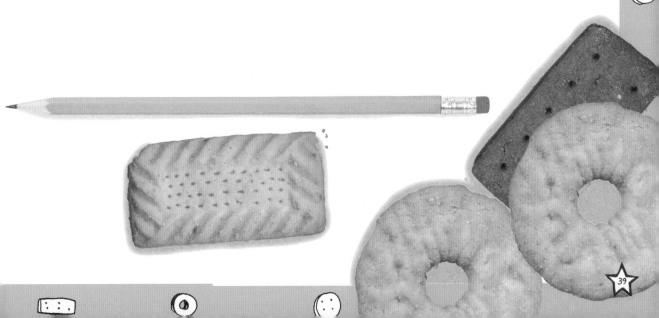

WHAT giant chocolate biscuit?

Ha! Ha!
(Mr Fullerman's beady EYES)

Here's a pyramid of MY TOP 5 biscuits. What are yours?

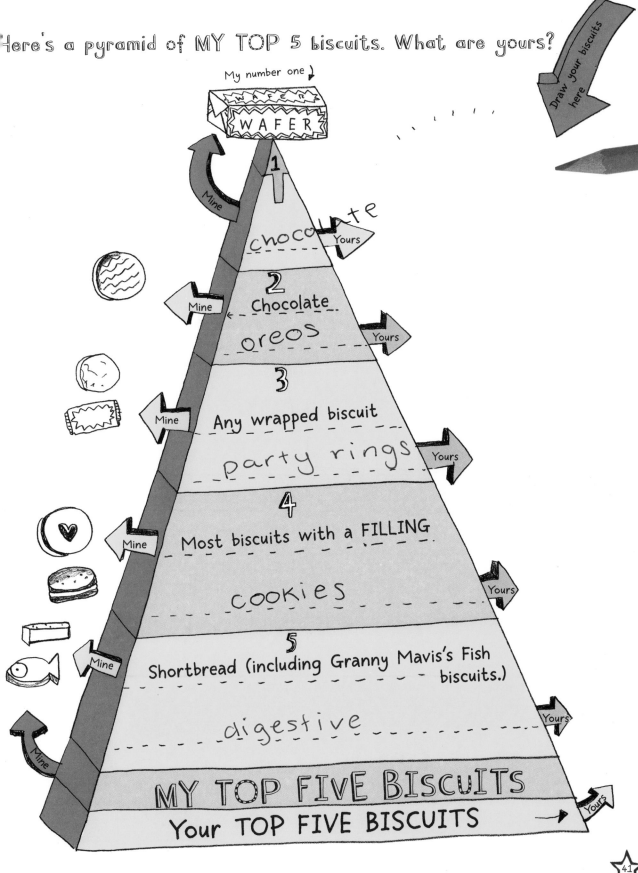

My number one

Draw your biscuits here

WAFER

1
Mine — chocolate — Yours

2
Mine — Chocolate oreos — Yours

3
Mine — Any wrapped biscuit — party rings — Yours

4
Mine — Most biscuits with a FILLING — cookies — Yours

5
Mine — Shortbread (including Granny Mavis's Fish biscuits.) — digestive — Yours

MY TOP FIVE BISCUITS
Your TOP FIVE BISCUITS

This is my emergency **Biscuit box** Most of the time

it's pretty empty. (I have a lot of emergencies.)

But right now it's SO stuffed with broken biscuits,

I can only just about get the lid on. I don't even have room to squeeze

in the three chocolate fingers I found in the kitchen (an unexpected FIND).

If I leave them out, SOMEONE (Mum Dad Delia) will take them.

So I'm looking for a NEW hiding place, when I HEAR

Granny Mavis and Grandad Bob downstairs.

They often POP round to see us (which is nice).

I put the chocolate fingers in my school bag (because no one

will look in there) then go downstairs to say HELLO!

Granny is telling Grandad to take off his HAT

so he can hear better (it's over his ears).

Did you say take out my teeth?

Grandad asks her.

Sometimes I think Grandad pretends he can't hear

very well so he can make a joke and be funny (like now!).

"Hello Grandad," I say. "Shall I take your hat for you?"

"You've got a CAT?" he asks me.

"No, but I'd like a dog," I say, as I can hear Rooster barking outside.

(sigh)

woof

Granny tells us she's brought us all a TREAT.

"It's a new recipe I've tried," she says.

Normally, I'd be pleased about TREATS but I've had loads lately,

so I'm not that bothered.

BUT when Granny brings out the CAKE, Mum, Dad and me go

"THAT LOOKS AMAZING!" I say.

"It's a CARROT CAKE,"

Granny tells us.

Which is Dad's favourite (and I like the look of the icing).

Mum gets some plates and a knife and Dad says he'll make some tea.

BUT there's a problem when Mum tries to CUT it.

"The knife's STUCK," she says. So Dad has a go.

But the CAKE starts to BREAK UP and the icing goes all mushy.

It looks a MESS now!

"Don't worry..." Dad says, spooning the cake MUSH on to plates.

"I'm sure it TASTES delicious."

"What have you done!" Granny says.

"I'll still have some!" Grandad tells us.

I'm looking at the cake, when I see something inside.

"Is that a WHOLE CARROT?" I ask.

"OF course it is ... it's a CARROT CAKE!" Granny says.

Mum and Dad are laughing.

"You're supposed to GRATE it into tiny pieces!" Mum tells her.

"Whoops-a-daisy!" Granny laughs too.

(Luckily, Granny has also brought

Fish biscuits – which I really like.)

GRANNY MAVIS'S FISH BISCUIT RECIPE

(They don't actually taste like fish ... just shortbread!)

wash your hands PLEASE!

AND get an adult to help you with the HOT STUFF (oven), and the SHARP STUFF (knife). (No accidents please!)

Ingredients

125g softened butter

50g caster sugar — Caster Sugar

175g plain flour — Plain Flour

spoon

sieve

rolling pin

mixing bowl

Greaseproof paper

Plus white icing sugar and raisins (for the eyes)

1. Pre-heat the oven to 180°c/350°f – gas mark 4.

2. Weigh out the plain flour and sieve into a bowl – then add the caster sugar.

3. Add the 125g of butter, then gently rub all the ingredients together until it looks like breadcrumbs.

4. Mix the dough into a ball shape. (Add a tiny bit of milk if it needs it.)

5. Gently roll out the mixture. Dust the surface and rolling pin with flour to stop it from sticking.

6. Carefully cut out a fish shape from the dough and place on the greaseproof paper on the tin.

7. Prick the biscuits with a fork and put them in the oven for 15-20 minutes until golden.

8. Then get an adult to help you take them out when cooked. Allow them to cool on a rack. Then to make the EYES you can use a BLOB of icing and a raisin.

Try making your own FISH biscuits and drawing them here

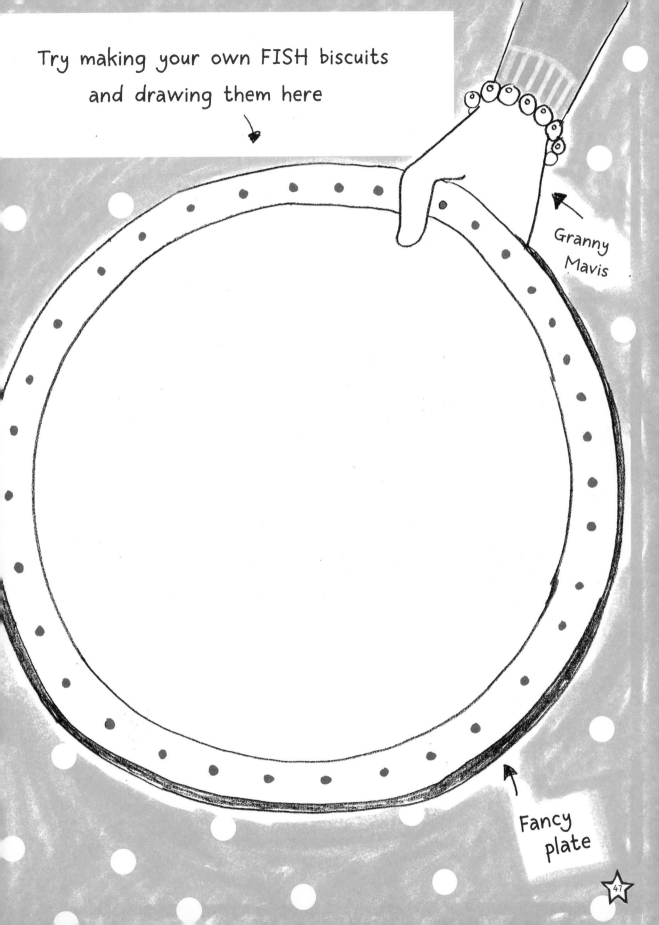

Granny Mavis

Fancy plate

How many pairs of Granddad's teeth can you find? 13

How many fish biscuits has he taken a nibble from? 7

Mr Fullerman has asked us to "MAKE UP" our very own CREATURE or animal. Which is exactly the sort of work I really LIKE doing.

While I'm drawing, Marcus is LOOKING at my page and says, "Why are you drawing monsters? Monsters are for KIDS." Then he adds,

I'm going to draw something FIERCE

Marcus bug
Agh!

BUGS

"Good for you, Marcus," I say and carry on drawing. BUT Marcus keeps staring at MY work and doesn't draw anything. He watches EVERYTHING I do.

Then when he FINALLY starts his drawing, it's a MONSTER (LIKE MINE!).
"I thought you said monsters are JUST FOR KIDS?" I ask him.
"I've changed my mind," Marcus tells me (SMUGLY).
I try and ignore him and carry on colouring my BUGS and MONSTERS.
I can see he's still STARING, so I add a few interesting BUGS which, funnily enough, he doesn't try and copy.

WHAT monster?

Create your own
MONSTER here

Yo!

TOM GATES

STYLE!

Yum, y

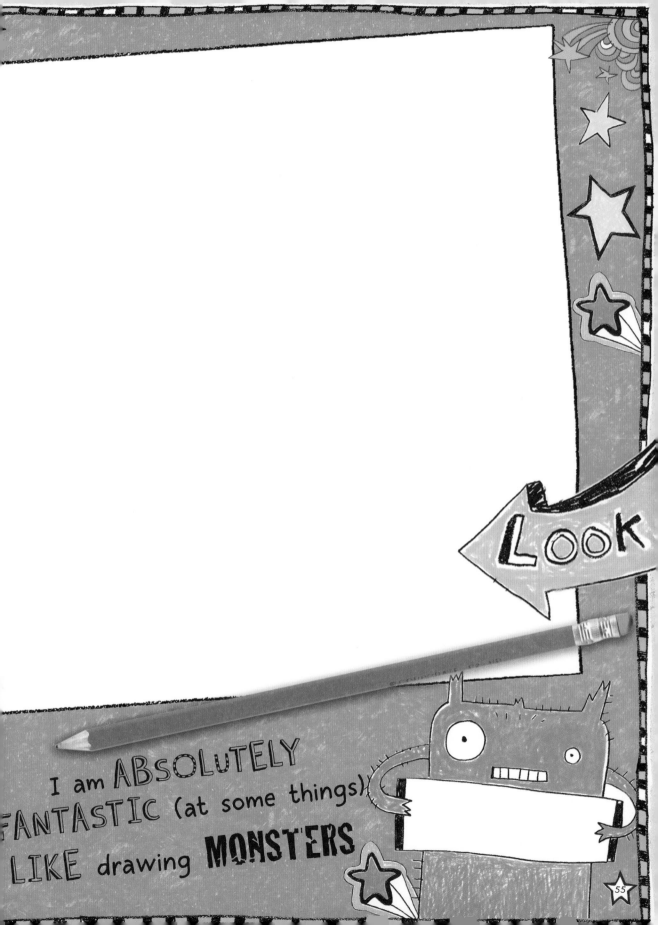

LOOk

I am ABSOLUTELY
FANTASTIC (at some things)
LIKE drawing MONSTERS

Me and Derek are having a GREAT time drawing,  eating nice snacks, doing ROCK STAR poses and ☉ ☉ looking at his dad's record collection.
"Does he know you've got these?" I ask Derek.
"Sort of," he says. "Dad makes me MIX TAPES so I don't use his record player." Derek holds up a CD with MIX TAPE written on it (which is confusing). "He puts all HIS favourite songs on them. I think there's some of June's dad's band, **PLASTIC CUP**, on here. Shall we have a listen?" "Why not? Could be funny!" Derek has just put on the CD when Delia BARGES in and says:

HEY - DUDE 2 ... that better not be my Rock Weekly you've got. OR my sunglasses! Does your dad know you've got his records, Derek?

Derek says, "Yes,"
then whispers, "sort of".
I tell Delia, "Close the door behind you, will you?"
hoping she'll GO.

But Delia doesn't BUDGE. Then she SPOTS the **PLASTIC CUP** album on my bed and asks, "Isn't that our next-door neighbour's band?"

"Yes, that's right," Derek says.

"BYE, DELIA," I tell her, but she ignores me.

"What kind of music is it?" she asks (annoyingly).

Then, Delia does something VERY UNEXPECTED and NOT very welcome at all...

Delia's Rock Weekly

PLASTIC CUP

(I'm always losing my socks. Can you spot them ... and my caramel wafers too?)

DELIA SITS DOWN ON MY BED!

NO!

PLASTIC CUP

"WHAT ARE YOU DOING?"
I ask her – because I can't BELIEVE she's in MY ROOM.

Delia ignores me, picks up the **PLASTIC CUP** album cover and says,

"Is this track four playing now?" I don't want to encourage her to
STAY even longer ... so I don't tell her it's Derek's mix tape playing.
I say NOTHING. But then Derek says,

"Yes – I think it is." Which makes Delia look at the album
cover even more.

"This album's actually quite good," Delia says.
"Why don't you take it to your OWN room then?"
I tell her thinking THAT might do the trick.

(It doesn't.)

Derek **PANICS**  and adds,

"DON'T TAKE IT AWAY! It's my dad's favourite album."

Delia **LAUGHS.** "Don't worry, squirts, I'm not going anywhere."

Derek looks relieved, but I just want her **OUT OF MY ROOM!**

I'm thinking about **HOW**  I'm going to make this

happen when SUDDENLY Mum walks past the OPEN DOOR.

She STOPS and looks **SURPRISED.**

This is nice to see – all of you together!

Mum says, smiling at us.

 "Yeah, right." Delia mumbles. "Quality time with the kids."

So I take the opportunity of Mum being here to take back
the **PLASTIC CUP** album and say,

"Delia's just leaving because we have to give all the albums
BACK to Derek's dad – don't we Derek?"

"Yes we do," Derek says. →

Delia takes the HINT (at last) and gets up to go.

But on the way OUT she take back her copy of Rock Weekly,
her sunglasses AND helps herself ...

TO MY CARAMEL WAFERS

If you don't want me in your room, DON'T take MY STUFF! Thanks for the wafers...

huh!

Before I can say anything ... SHE'S GONE (with my wafers).

I'm glad she's out of my room. BUT I'M MAD she's pinched my wafers. "THAT DOES IT!" I say to Derek, "I'm making a special sign to keep HER OUT of my room."

Good idea Derek says, while he picks up his dad's album covers and takes back his mix tape.

"I'll make one for when we have band practice."

It's a GOOD plan. So that's what we do.

(I hope it works.)

Use this as a template if you want to make your own.

Something to KEEP OUT incredibly ANNOYING OLDER SISTERS (or BROTHERS!) (or FAMILY!)

KEEP OUT!
(Especially DELIA)

CUT around the edge and hang on the handle of your door. Get an adult to help.

COME IN

BRING BISCUITS

My sign seems to be working. So I use it when I'm in the bathroom, kitchen and when I'm watching TV too. It's driving Delia NUTS! Can you SPOT THE DIFFERENCE?

How to do a BREAKFAST DOODLE

BANANA doodle

Start with a fresh banana.

Take a cocktail stick (mind the sharp end).

CAREFULLY Push the stick into the banana skin – not too deeply.

Wherever you prick a hole, the banana will turn black.

You can do a doodle like this quite quickly.

But don't leave it too long before you eat it. It goes darker and darker (then goes mouldy – yuck).

TOAST doodle

← Nice fresh bread

Clean hands

Take a slice of bread.
Press the bread down with your fingers like this, making dents in the bread.

Then **TOAST** the bread. (Make sure you get an adult to help!) The TOAST will go brown, but stay white where you've pressed down.

TA DA! Yum.

PLAY the GAME

STAR PUPIL

Mr Fullerman reminds us that he'll be choosing NEW STAR PuPILS before the OPEN DAY, which is coming up soon. (OPEN DAY is when new kids and parents come to look round the school.)

"AND a few of our class will be asked to be EXTRA HELPERS too," he adds.

"If you've NOT been a STAR PUPIL before and you've given in your homework on time, you might get the chance to be one THIS time," he tells us.

THINGS YOU NEED
- Glue
- Coloured pencils
- Scissors (safety ones are best)
- Photos of you and your friends
- A piece of card

READ
THIS!
↓

Use pencils to colour in the counters. Draw your own self-portrait or stick your photo on some of them.

MAKE your own DICE...

If you don't have any dice, you can make your own by following these simple instructions:
1. Cut out the dice template
2. Stick it to a thin piece of card & fold along the lines
3. Stick the dice together by gluing the flaps to the underside

Find out
HOW YOU DID!

QUIZ page 16-17

1. c) Sunglasses
2. b) Rooster
3. c) DUDE3
4. a) Caramel Wafer
5. d) Mr Keen
6. c) The Fossils
7. a) Doodling
8. b) A banana
9. c) Derek
10. a) Delia's a weirdo
11. c) Not very much
12. c) Marcus and Amy
13. c) Mrs Worthingtash

MAZE page 42-43

TOM can't find his secret stash of caramel wafers!   Help him uncover them before ROOSTER does.

START

What ever?

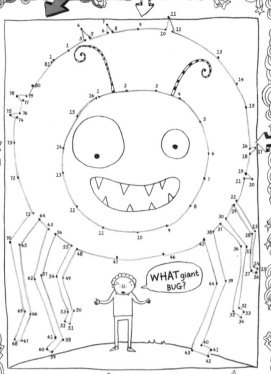

DOT-TO-DOT page 52-53

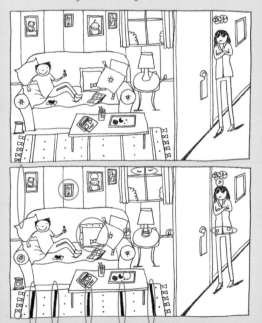

My sign seems to be working. So I use it when I'm in the bathroom, kitchen and when I'm watching TV too. It's driving Delia NUTS! Can you SPOT THE DIFFERENCE?

SPOT THE DIFFERENCE
page 63

Sooo many answers

THERE ARE
13 PAIRS OF
TEETH ON page 48-49

SPOT THE DIFFERENCE
page 64-65

VOCALS, PIANO, DRUMS, UKULELE, RECORDER, GUITAR.

Learn to play the songs from the books.

Download the Tom Gates Music app to help you practise!